The Irresistible

JIM DAVIS

Sophie
Barnes

ℛℛ
RAVETTE PUBLISHING

© 1997 PAWS INCORPORATED
(www.garfield.com)

First published by
Ravette Publishing Limited 1997

Printed and bound in Great Britain
for Ravette Publishing Limited,
Unit 3, Tristar Centre,
Star Road, Partridge Green,
West Sussex RH13 8RA
by Cox & Wyman Ltd, Reading, Berkshire

ISBN 1 85304 940 9

SNIFF
SNIFF
SNIFF

AH **HA!!** **NOG** BREATH!

CURSES

JIM DAVIS 12-20

JIM DAVIS 12-30

WHAT A BEAUTIFUL, SUNNY DAY!

JIM DAVIS 3-7

CREAM IN YOUR COFFEE, GARFIELD?

© 1995 PAWS, INC./Distributed by Universal Press Syndicate

JIM DAVIS 3·16

I'M SORRY! DID I OFFEND YOUR SENSE OF AESTHETICS?!

Cream

THE CAPTAIN APOLOGIZES FOR THE SLIGHT TURBULENCE

THIS ALSO CONCLUDES THE MEAL PORTION OF YOUR FLIGHT

© 1995 PAWS, INC./Distributed by Universal Press Syndicate

© 1995 PAWS, INC./Distributed by Universal Press Syndicate

C'MON, MOUSE... LET GO!

SAY "PRETTY PLEASE WITH A CHERRY ON TOP"

JIM DAVIS 4-22

LOUSY WEATHER WE'RE HAVING

NOT IF YOU DON'T GET OUT OF BED!

JIM DAVIS 4-24

JIM DAVIS 4-26

© 1985 PAWS, INC./Distributed by Universal Press Syndicate

JIM DAVIS 5-4

OTHER GARFIELD BOOKS IN THIS SERIES

| A Garfield Christmas | £3.99 |
| Garfield's Thanksgiving | £2.95 |

GARFIELD THEME BOOKS

Garfield's Guide to Behaving Badly	£3.99
Garfield's Guide to Insults	£3.99
Garfield's Guide to Pigging Out	£3.99
Garfield's Guide to Romance	£3.99

All Ravette books are available at your local bookshop or from the address below. Just tick the titles required and send the form with your remittance to:-

B.B.C.S., P.O. BOX 941, HULL, NORTH HUMBERSIDE HU1 3YQ
24 Hour Telephone Credit Card Line 01482 224626
Prices and availability are subject to change without notice.

Please enclose a cheque or postal order made payable to B.B.C.S. to the value of the cover price of the book and allow the following for postage and packing:

| U.K. & B.F.P.O: | £1.00 for the first book and 50p for each additional book to a maximum of £3.50. |
| Overseas & Eire | £2.00 for the first book, £1.00 for the second and 50p for each additional book. |

BLOCK CAPITALS PLEASE

Name ....

Address...

....

....

Cards accepted: Mastercard and Visa

Expiry Date ....Signature ....